mac's year

1996

Cartoons from the *Daily Mail*

Stan McMurtry mac
Edited by Mark Bryant

ORION

For Cecil and Dorothy

Orion Books
A Division of the Orion Publishing Group Ltd
Orion House
5 Upper St Martin's Lane
London WC2H 9EA

First published by Orion 1996

ISBN 0 75280 622 X

Printed and bound in Great Britain by
The Guernsey Press Co. Ltd, Guernsey, C. I.

'No, fat man with funny moustache doesn't want a liquorice toffee –
fat man with funny moustache wants to draw some money out!'

14 August　　Holidaymakers 'dropped like flies' when a 12-hour mystery virus swept through Pontin's holiday camp in Torquay, Devon, only three weeks after an outbreak of salmonella at the company's resort in Blackpool.

'Look on the bright side, Mr Watkins, you're a dead cert to win the knobbly knees competition.'

'Wonderful. I just hope he doesn't have to put up with any silly remarks about falling standards.'

21 August   As World War II veterans who had served in Burma and the Far East marched
down the Mall to commemorate the 50th anniversary of V-J Day, the refusal of
the Japanese government to apologize for wartime atrocities still rankled with many.

At the going down of the sun and in the morning we will remember them.

'. . . and this is the new, hi-tech, John Gummer water-saving bathroom . . .'

24 August　When hosepipe bans were introduced, despite a very wet winter in 1994, water-industry watchdog Ofwat warned water companies that they could face huge bills for compensation if customers were forced to collect water from the street.

'If that's someone seeking compensation, Hoskins, give him a quick squirt with the hosepipe.'

'Who'd have thought it – Michael Barrymore living a lie for 19 years?'

28 August   After allegations of sexual misconduct with parishioners at the popular weekly 'Nine O'Clock' rock-music church service begun in Sheffield in 1978, 38-year-old Rev. Chris Brain was banned from preaching in Britain.

'. . . and for those among us who are unaware of our usual timetable, there will be no Nine O'Clock Service this week or any other week . . .'

29 August Serb gunners continued to massacre civilians with impunity as they bombarded the Bosnian capital of Sarajevo, despite its status as one of four remaining 'safe areas' which UN forces had pledged to defend against attack.

31 August   Illuminated overhead signs indicating rush-hour speed limits were introduced on a stretch of the M25 near Heathrow Airport, London, in an experimental scheme to ease traffic congestion.

'Yes, sir. The new lights slowed the M25 traffic a little, but we couldn't have done it without our WPC Gribshaw . . .'

'Quickly, Gerald, my smelling salts! A member of the aristocracy has been accused of threatening dire deeds to his wife . . .'

11 September   On the eve of his speech to the TUC Conference, Labour leader Tony Blair criticized ultra-Left dissidents who believed that only a return to old-style Labour policies would win the next election, saying they needed 'therapy'.

'The one at the end is a complete nut – he quite likes Tony Blair's policies.'

'Now think hard, children. Was leaving Mrs Conway buried overnight in our sand area right or wrong?'

'Honestly, love, I didn't wolf-whistle. My sandwich tin squeaked.'

'Excuse me, sir. The office staff have had a bit of a whip-round . . .'

'Hello, love – and what bargains have you picked up today?'

29 September   In a judgment that Deputy Prime Minister Michael Heseltine branded as 'ludicrous', the European Court of Human Rights ruled that the killing of three unarmed IRA suspects by the British Army in Gibraltar in 1988 was unjustified.

'Dear Sirs, thanks to your decision let's hope the streets will now be safe for decent citizens to go about their business without some murderin' Brit soldier creeping up from behind and . . .'

'I do hope you like sausages – I haven't quite got the hang of this new metrication yet.'

'. . . Once again, Mr Blair, you are stealing Tory ideas. We here at Conservative Central Office have been using lap-top computers for years . . .'

9 October   Alan Howarth, Tory MP for Stratford-upon-Avon, defected to Labour on the eve of the Conservative Party conference in Blackpool, claiming that many others who supported 'social justice' and traditional Conservatism were ready to follow.

'I'm afraid there have been a few more overnight defections.'

'Are you awake, Father? It's me, Elizabeth Hurley.'

12 October At the Tory conference tough new measures to clamp road-tax dodgers were proposed and a steering group, featuring ITN newscaster Trevor McDonald, was set up to combat falling standards in spoken and written English in schools.

'He was cursing and swearing about the Tories clamping our untaxed car when suddenly Trevor McDonald appeared . . .'

'It's my opinion, Marjorie, that your weekly *Knitters and Crocheters* magazine is not what it was . . .'

'So, the Tory Left want me gagged? Huh! And how do they hope to achieve that?'

20 October Anthea Turner, presenter of BBC TV's 'National Lottery Live' programme, announced that she would be moving to ITV. New contracts with Carlton and GMTV amounting to over £1 million a year would make her one of TV's highest earners.

'False alarm, dear. It's only Anthea Turner's pay-packet going by . . .'

23 October   Rumours abounded that the 34-year-old British actor, Hugh Grant, would star
as the disgraced derivatives trader, Nick Leeson, in a film to be produced by
Sir David Frost about the collapse of Barings Bank.

'Dear Hugh Grant, I am serving a one-month sentence for habitually robbing my gas meter.
I write to offer you the exciting opportunity of playing me in a true-life, big-screen blockbuster . . .'

9 November   Local residents living near Manchester Airport had a scare when the pilot of a Britannia Airways Boeing 767 holiday jet bound for Ibiza flew very low over his home in Congleton, Cheshire, in a stunt to wish his wife a happy birthday.

'All together now. As we fly through her bedroom let's all sing "Happy Birthday" to the pilot's wife . . .'

10 November 60-year-old Neighbourhood Watch leader, Jon Pratchett, was cleared in court after shooting and wounding two burglars who had broken into his wine warehouse in Borough Green, Kent.

'You're doing a fine job, Miss Molesworthy, but the residents' association is a little concerned about a missing postman, the milkman, two newspaper boys and Mr Cartwright's cat.'

'Here comes Mum now – why not ask her opinion?'

14 November   National Heritage Secretary Virginia Bottomley outlawed the American-backed
Swedish 'TV Erotica' satellite channel. Meanwhile, a new Parliamentary
Commissioner was appointed to monitor MPs' behaviour in the wake of the Nolan Report.

'We don't want to be banned in Britain, Ingrid. So at this point you turn to the cameras,
flutter your eyelashes and give a party political speech on behalf of the Conservatives . . .'

16 November Without the prior knowledge or approval of Buckingham Palace, Princess Diana appeared in a 60-minute interview for BBC TV's 'Panorama' programme and revealed secrets about her marriage to Prince Charles.

'Good news, Ma'am. The producer of "Panorama" has agreed to put on a Bugs Bunny cartoon instead.'

17 November   Schoolgirl Leah Betts of Latchingdon, Essex, died five days after taking a tablet of the drug Ecstasy at a party to celebrate her 18th birthday.

ECSTASY: An overwhelming feeling of joy or rapture (*Oxford English Dictionary*).

'That's Dempsey – she's claiming compensation for wrongful arrest.'

'It's either a very small lottery win or a Kenneth Clarke tax cut.'

30 November   As US President Clinton visited the UK, the prestigious £20,000 Turner Prize for modern art was won by 30-year-old Damien Hirst, whose *Mother and Child, Divided* consisted of a cow and calf sliced in half and preserved in formaldehyde.

'The chef's special won the Turner Prize. How would you like it done?'

'I feel I must warn you, I ate a beef sandwich an hour ago.'

'Stop moaning. If that woman next door's husband can have a planet named after him, so can mine.'

14 December As the 'Mad Cow' debate continued, medical chiefs attacked the 'irresponsibility and bad timing' of Health Secretary Stephen Dorrell's relaxation of safe drinking limits only a week after launching a hard-hitting drink-driving offensive.

'Oh, no! I think Clarissa's got Mad Human Disease.'

'A bit disappointing, really. His beard's gone, he's got a black eye and he doesn't say, "Ho, Ho, Ho" – he says, "*** off!"'

19 December   Prime Minister John Major struggled to avert a Commons defeat as Tory MPs threatened to resign over a directive from Brussels for a massive cut in Britain's fish quotas which could slash UK catches in half.

'Oh, Kevin. You haven't gone and exceeded the British fishing quotas again, have you?'

'Dinna get too excited, Moira. But if I win the £40 million lottery jackpot this weekend, I might lash out on a couple of new buckets.'

9 January   A hospital trust in Essex started a Health Service merry-go-round when it
began to headhunt specialist nurses from its rivals with offers of a 'golden hello'
worth up to £2000.

'The nurse who usually does this got 'ead-'unted half an hour ago, dearie – trousers orf!'

'Stand by! An estate agent and two customers approaching the front gate . . . five . . . four . . . three . . . two . . .'

12 January Lord Chancellor Mackay introduced his controversial Divorce Bill which removed the concept of fault, cut the maximum waiting period from five years to one, and allowed one partner to sue for divorce irrespective of the other's wishes.

'I want a "no-fault" divorce – pass it on.'

'. . . anyway, there I was waiting for me bus 'ome, when up walks Prince Philip, completely starkers, walkin' the corgis. "'Ello, darlin'," he says, grabbin' me by the . . .'

16 January   There were fears that Princess Diana was straying into politics when she took her sons William (13) and Harry (11) to visit a shelter for the homeless in London's Soho, run by the charity Centrepoint, of which she is patron.

'Oh, no! Not William and Harry again!'

'Okay, yah! Hand one the jolly old boodle and be awfully dashed quick about it, what!'

23 January   There was much discussion in the tabloid press when Sarah Cook,
a 13-year-old schoolgirl from Braintree, Essex – and judged a minor under English law –
married a Turkish waiter she had met on holiday the previous year.

'. . . The good news is Fiona's back from her school trip to Turkey . . .'

25 January   Labour Health spokesperson, Harriet Harman, was accused of hypocrisy for
sending her son to a grant-maintained grammar school in opposition to Party policy.
Meanwhile, public debate grew increasingly heated over the Sarah Cook marriage.

'I'm not going to be a hypocrite and send 'er to no grammar school.
I've put 'er name down for a Turkish waiter when she's eleven.'

29 January   As another huge 'rollover' lottery jackpot was announced, the Duchess of York looked set to become the first member of the Royal Family to be taken to court when she faced a writ for the return of a personal loan of £100,000.

'. . . we thank you for all your letters and are sorry to hear of your reduced circumstances, but as our lottery win was only ten pounds, Duchess, I'm afraid . . .'

30 January   Tony Blair came under heavy attack from Tory MPs when he announced plans
for an accelerated learning scheme to allow brighter schoolchildren to be 'fast-tracked',
despite Labour's long-standing official position condemning streaming.

'. . . thanks to you, Mr Blair, I have fast-tracked through primary school,
secondary school and university. You have made me what I am today – a Tory.'

'Yes, Madam Speaker. When I went into hospital this morning for a routine check-up, I thought I detected a tiny trace of resentment over our demands for 100% pay-rises . . .'

"... Golly, gosh!" the plucky little helicopter cried, "while we were asleep the nasty, horrid bailiff men have been ...'"

6 February   A study by the Association of Chief Police Officers to promote a new 'public-friendly' image for the Force recommended phasing out the traditional police helmet – except in London, where they were still seen as a tourist attraction.

'Twenty-five years I've worn a helmet and I'm not changing now!'

'Remember the good old days of 1996 . . . just before Tony Blair scrapped all hereditary titles?'

12 February As Sinn Fein leader Gerry Adams continued to resist demands for the decommissioning of weapons before peace talks could begin, the IRA ended its 17-month ceasefire with a huge bomb in a car park in Canary Wharf, London.

'In response to the British Government's demands that the IRA get rid of their weapons, they have just disposed of half a ton of explosives . . .'

'Good news, Mr Winkworth – we've grown you a brand new heart in our laboratory . . .'

16 February Sir Richard Scott's 2400-page report into the arms-to-Iraq affair was finally published, but despite heavy criticism of ministers who had tried to lay the blame on 'supergun' manufacturers Matrix Churchill, there were no resignations.

'Apparently the Prime Minister got Matrix Churchill to make a huge gun . . .'

19 February Lord Chancellor Mackay tabled an amendment to his Divorce Bill to allow children the chance to block their parents' separation if there were grounds for believing that a couple's divorce would damage their offsprings' emotional needs.

'This insistence that I tidy my room is a clear abdication by both of you of your domestic responsibilities and highlights your hollow sham of a marriage – I've applied for a divorce for you . . .'

20 February   A double-decker bus blew up in the Strand, in London's theatreland, injuring passengers and killing an Irishman believed to be carrying explosives to another IRA target in the city.

'It's not all bad news then . . .'

'Apparently there was something wrong with the last group photograph.'

26 February   The Department of Social Security announced that it was to appoint resident liaison officers in Bangladesh and Pakistan to administer annual payments of benefits worth over £12 million to pensioners who formerly worked in Britain.

'I'm sorry, due to a clerical error, your payments from now on will be made through our new Bangladesh office . . . you take a number eight bus to Euston, then . . .'

'He doesn't usually take to strangers. We bought him to annoy our next-door neighbour.'

1 March After sustained pressure from Buckingham Palace, Princess Diana finally agreed to divorce Prince Charles. There was considerable speculation about the exact nature of the financial settlement for the fitness-obsessed princess.

'It must be part of the divorce settlement.'

5 March   Tory backbenchers feared an illegal immigration 'nightmare' when the Prime Minister decided to grant two million Hong Kong Chinese short-term visa-free entry to the UK when the Crown colony is handed back to China next year.

'So that's agreed then? I call a general election, two million of you come over, vote Tory then go home again . . .'

8 March   The scientific journal, *Nature*, reported that the first ever sheep to be cloned from a single embryo had been born last July at the Government-funded Roslin Institute research centre near Edinburgh.

'Of course, it wasn't an instant success. We had a lot of failures to begin with . . . down, boy!'

'Don't disturb Daddy. He's preparing a case against a whisky company.'

'It's not been Frank's weekend – fancy forgetting to send his mother a Mother's Day card.'

19 March   National Heritage Secretary Virginia Bottomley agreed to evaluate the 'V-chip' –
a computerized device for scrambling TV transmissions which would give parents power
to veto programmes they felt unsuitable for their children.

'Actually, George, there is another way of stopping the children watching sex and violence
when we're out – it's called a V-chip.'

21 March Champion golfer, Philomena Vaughn, won her case for unfair dismissal when she was sacked from her job at Dewstow Golf Club, Caerwent, Wales, after she punched a member who touched her leg in the bar.

'I do wish the Ladies' Champion would shout "Fore" prior to striking a member.'

22 March After a decade of fudge and denial, the Government admitted that there may, after all, be a link between Mad Cow Disease and CJD in humans. With 14,000 new cases being identified in cattle each year, a massive cull looked inevitable.

'Don't scoff, I once saw Steve McQueen do this in a film . . .'

25 March   Because of the BSE risk, McDonald's fast-food chain – buyers of the equivalent of one in every 12 cows slaughtered in the UK – announced that it would no longer use British beef in burgers at its 670 restaurants.

'C'mon, c'mon, we've got customers waiting! Tap him on the head and put him in the mincer.'

28 March A remarkable series of photos published in *Hello!* magazine showed the Duchess of York, transformed by heavy make-up, looking like an advertising model or, as some detractors had it, like Morticia in TV's 'The Addams Family'.

'For the last time, Duchess. No thanks. We've got enough!'

15 April   Britain's Nick Faldo won the US Masters golf tournament at Augusta, Georgia. Meanwhile, veteran American evangelist Billy Graham toured the UK.

'You say you were glued to the TV yesterday, Paterson. Was that for the US Masters golf tournament or Billy Graham?'

19 April Grieving relatives awaiting the hearse at Maureen Jones's cottage in Thwing, Humberside, received a shock when the 59-year-old widow, officially pronounced dead by her GP after collapsing into a coma, came back to life.

'I told you that doctor was incompetent!'

22 April   As the trials and tribulations continued amongst the junior members of the Royal Family, Her Majesty the Queen celebrated her 70th birthday.

'All our children and their spouses to Jupiter? Oh, Philip. You spoil me . . .'

'£925 million losses and you were expecting a big, expensive, fuel-guzzling train?'

25 April   After a massive internal Tory rebellion – led by four Cabinet ministers and more than 130 backbenchers – an amendment was made to the bill on family law reform to extend the 'cooling off' period before divorce from 12 to 18 months.

'. . . and then, guess what? I rebelled against the Government's divorce reforms. You should've seen Major's face. Was I worried? Not a bit. Well, anyway . . . are you listening, darling?'

26 April   Teachers at Glaisdale Comprehensive School in Bilborough, Nottingham, threatened strike action when an appeal board ruled that a 13-year-old tearaway pupil, who had been expelled for violent and disruptive behaviour, should be reinstated.

'Say hello to your new teacher, Richard . . . RICHARD!'

30 April   As complaints against British Gas reached a record 49,104, a pilot scheme was introduced in the West Country to allow independent companies – offering tariff discounts of up to 21% – to compete for domestic supply.

'He was ever such a good salesman, dear.'

'Of all the days to announce his sex-change, he has to choose today!'

3 May   When the votes had been counted, the Tories were soundly defeated in the local government elections. The loss of 600 council seats fuelled speculation that Deputy Prime Minister Michael Heseltine might soon replace John Major.

'Yes, terribly depressing results, Prime Minister. I'm on my way over now to offer support, sympathy and helpful advice . . .'

'So, what did the lady at the sex-discrimination board say when you complained?'

7 May A scheme by the Royal Town Planning Institute to give disadvantaged ethnic minorities special rights to build mosques, open takeaways etc, was condemned by Tory MPs for introducing double standards and threatening urban harmony.

'The Nanooks wouldn't have got permission for that if they'd been British.'

'Isn't it wonderful news? The Russians aren't going to expel us after all . . .'

13 May   Princess Diana went on holiday to Majorca. A few weeks earlier she caused a storm of controversy by attending a heart-surgery operation on an African boy at London's Harefield Hospital to help promote a new children's health charity.

'The Princess gets bored on the beach.'

'Let's all be terribly brave, shall we, children? We've got a nice new problem-child joining us today . . .'

16 May   An inquiry was ordered when traces of RDX, a component of the IRA's favourite explosive Semtex, were found to have contaminated equipment at the Government's forensic laboratory, casting doubt on the convictions of 38 terror suspects.

'Don't forget, Doris. From now on we've got to dust the shelves, mop the floors and take a wet rag to any microscopic RDX particles what's lurkin' in the centrifuge-holder of the bomb-analysis machine . . .'

20 May   As the fear of IRA bombers on the mainland continued, allegations were made that the Tory Party had accepted cash donations from a businessman linked to the Bosnian Serb leader and alleged war criminal, Radovan Karadic.

'It's all right, sir, it's not the IRA. It's the Bosnian Serbs.'

21 May   Shares in the newly privatized company, Railtrack, soared on their first day of
trading, giving instant profits to thousands of small investors.

'Never mind how well your shares did – blow into this!'

23 May Furious that two months of diplomacy had failed to lift the ban on British beef exports to Europe, Prime Minister John Major launched a war of attrition by boycotting all key EU business until the matter was resolved.

'Lads, meet John – John wants to pick up a few tips on how to be disruptive . . .'

'Okay, let's do a deal. You keep baby-milk and beef off the menu and I'll try to keep the costs down later on . . .'

30 May   Police were brought in to investigate allegations of damage to a Cathay Pacific Boeing 747 by the English football team after an in-flight party to celebrate Paul Gascoigne's 29th birthday on their return from a match in Hong Kong.

'Marvellous in-flight entertainment. Did you see how Gazza weaved between the stewardesses, passed to Ferdinand then shot past the pilot for a hat-trick?'

'Si, si, Mañuel, it might be a Breetish bluff. But I'm not taking any chances – hard astern!'

6 June　Europe's newest and biggest-ever unmanned space rocket, Ariane 5 –
carrying millions of pounds' worth of British satellite technology – was automatically
blown to pieces 40 seconds into its maiden flight when it veered off course.

'. . . then just as we launched, the bottle fell over . . .'

'Looks like another gas director has exploded.'

10 June   Pregnant 34-year-old, Janine O'Connor, serving 30 months for arson at London's Holloway Prison, escaped from the nearby Whittington Hospital when she was left unguarded after doctors diagnosed that she had suffered a false labour.

'Just to be on the safe side. When the baby appears, snap these on him.'

'I'm sorry, Marjorie, but Bernard is everything I want in a woman. He plays darts, likes a few pints, supports Arsenal and is willing to have the operation . . .'

13 June   Prime Minister John Major hit out at the National Lottery Charities Board when it was revealed that nearly £500,000 of lottery cash had been given to support-groups for homosexuals and prostitutes.

'I don't fancy you much either, but shove over, we may be in line for a lottery award . . .'

'It's from my pen-friend in England, I think. But due to a shameful deficiency in literary and numeracy over there, caused by deeply impregnated, progressive clap-trap teaching methods, I can barely read it.'

17 June   A 1000lb IRA bomb which exploded in one of Manchester's main shopping centres, injuring 200 and causing millions of pounds' worth of damage, left many doubting the sincerity of Sinn Fein's often-stated commitment to the peace process.

The Political Wing of the IRA

'Sorry I'm late, darling. Debating the new Divorce Bill till all hours, then had a few drinks with my secretary, then down to my club for . . . darling?'

20 June The new law on divorce, with its recommendations that counsellors should advise couples at every stage of the process, led to speculation that there would be a huge explosion in vacancies for Government-funded marriage-guidance specialists.

'Just ignore our new team of counsellors, Mrs Wagthorne . . . I believe you wanted a private discussion about a divorce.'

'It's one of our cows. I think she's altering her birth certificate.'

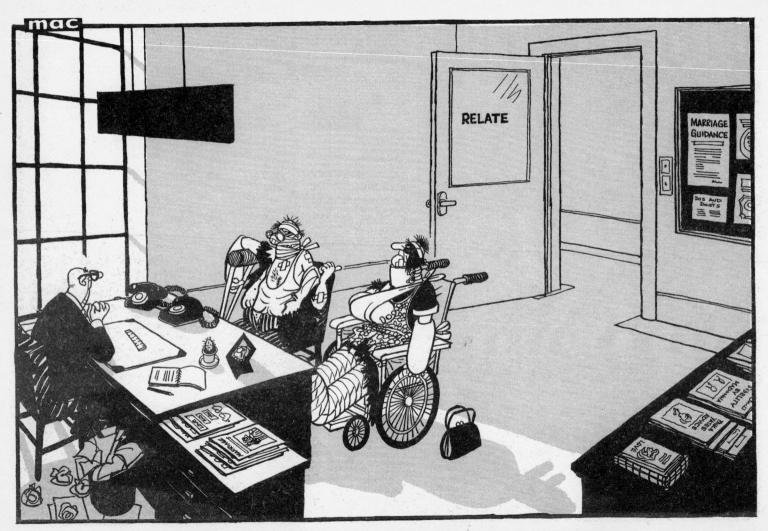

'. . . so she said, "It's my turn for the TV – Wimbledon's started," so I said, "Not till after Wednesday's semi-final," so she took a swipe at me, then I . . .'

'Hello there. And who's my lucky first patient?'

'Sorry we had to leave you last night. What a game! – now where were we?'

'Look, Boris Becker isn't to blame for the football. So from now on you gently lob one ball at a time to him – and no toilet rolls!'

1 July   Tory backbenchers accused the Government of breaking earlier pledges when
it proposed to sell off 60,000 MOD homes formerly occupied by Service
personnel in a move which was expected to raise £1.6 billion for the Treasury.

'Left, right, left, right . . . This is the sitting-room, two, three, four,
right wheel for the kitchen . . . wait for it, wait for it!'

2 July Soccer star Paul Gascoigne married former model Sheryl Kyle. 'Gazza', who had drunk alcohol while spread-eagled during a much-criticized incident in Hong Kong, imitated the act after scoring against Scotland in the European Cup.

'Please, Gazza. Just while we're on honeymoon, can't you have breakfast sitting up at the table like everyone else?'

4 July In what US President Clinton called 'a triumph for democracy', 65-year-old Boris Yeltsin beat his Communist opponent in the elections for Russian President, despite rumours of his increasing ill-health from alcoholism.

'Okay, comrades. A nice reassuring wave now, just to show them he's fit and sober.'

'In you go, Cook. I've just heard Mr Mandela say how sorry he was to miss the tennis highlights.'

11 July   Politicians defied their leaders and voted for a 26% pay rise for backbench MPs
with Cabinet Ministers' salaries rising to £103,000 and the Prime Minister
earning £143,000.

'. . . and while your Snookums Wookums was negotiating his big pay-rise,
what was his little Popsickle doing . . . ?'

'Mind the doors . . . Oh, good shot, Charlie . . . take her away!'

15 July   Though she received a lump-sum payment of £15 million, the terms of Princess Diana's divorce settlement were exacting, stripping her of the title 'Her Royal Highness' and forbidding her to travel abroad without Palace approval.

'Do you have to stay bitter right to the end, Charles? I did not want my £15 million in pennies!'

'Sex? I thought you'd popped out to change your specs.'

18 July In a move that took Buckingham Palace by surprise, Princess Diana – now no longer allowed to use her royal title – decided to cut her links with almost 100 charities, as she felt they deserved a royal patron.

'Since Princess Diana has dropped being involved with our Contagious Disease Charity, Ma'am, we wondered if we could persuade you to . . . Ma'am?

'When we get home I want to have a look at your microchip
to see what you were just thinking . . .'

22 July   As the blazing summer heat continued, stormclouds gathered over the private life of BBC TV's weather forecaster, Michael Fish, when it was revealed that he was having an affair with 42-year-old civil servant, Heather Arnold.

'I wish he'd hurry up and tell us if it's going to rain . . .'

23 July   During the opening ceremony for the 100th Olympic Games in Atlanta –
screened live before a TV audience of 3.5 billion – British canoeist Shaun
Pearce proposed on bended knee to team physiotherapist Julie Stark (she accepted).

'Not now, Norman!'

'There are only 152 shopping days till my Christmas speech.
Why not treat oneself to the fresh, zingy taste of real coffee and one's corgis to munchy-crunchy Doggy Mix . . .'

'Bernard, do as the doctor says – take off your lambswool socks!'

30 July   After months of protests against the excessive noise of bell-ringing by visiting campanologists, 64-year-old Mrs Midge Mather hacked through the door of St Swithun's church in Compton Bassett, Wiltshire, with an axe and cut the bell-ropes.

'And God sayeth, love thy neighbour as thyself, even though he alloweth the bells to peal a little too long for some tastes . . .'

'I expect you miss all this when you're on strike . . .'

2 August Former England cricketers Ian Botham and Allan Lamb faced a £500,000 legal bill after losing their libel case against Imran Khan over allegations that the former Pakistan captain had called them low-class racists and cheats.

'So I said, "Bad luck about the court case, Mr Botham", slapped a parking-ticket on his car then asked for his autograph for my family back in Pakistan . . .'